This edition published by Parragon Books Ltd in 2014 and distributed by

Parragon Inc.
440 Park Avenue South, 13th Floor
New York, NY 10016
www.parragon.com

ISBN 978-1-4723-5202-6

Printed in China

Black Beauty

Based on the original story by Anna Sewell
Retold by Catherine Allison

Illustrated by Livia Coloji

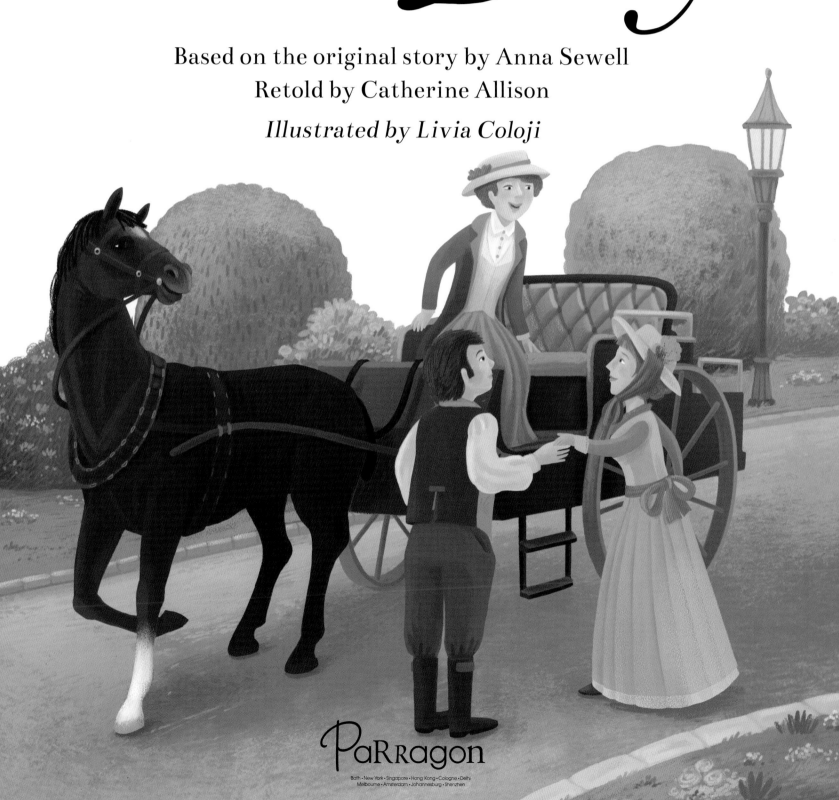

Parragon

Bath · New York · Singapore · Hong Kong · Cologne · Delhi
Melbourne · Amsterdam · Johannesburg · Shenzhen

When I was a very young foal, I lived in a pleasant meadow with a pond of clear water in it. In the daytime, I ran by my mother's side, and at night, I lay down close beside her. She was a wise old horse and used to tell me, "I hope you will grow up gentle and good, and never learn bad ways. Do your work with a good will, lift your feet up well when you trot, and never bite or kick, even in play." I have never forgotten her advice.

Our master was a kind man. He gave us good food and good lodging, and he spoke as kindly to us as he did to his own children. We were all fond of him.

I began to grow handsome: my coat was fine, soft, and black, and I had one white foot and a pretty white star on my forehead. My master broke me in himself, rather than leave it to one of his grooms. With a good deal of coaxing, oats, pats, and gentle words, he taught me to wear a saddle and bridle and to carry a man, woman, or child on my back, to go quietly, just the way they wished, and to pull a carriage by holding a bit. I didn't like the bit at all at first—it was a nasty thing to have cold metal in my mouth—but my mother always wore one when she went out, so at last, I got used to wearing it.

My mother always told me the better I behaved, the better I would be treated, and that I should always do my best to please my master. "I hope you will fall into good hands," she said, "but a horse never knows who may buy him or who may drive him. It is all down to chance for us, but still I say, do your best wherever you are, and keep up your good name."

I was four years old when I was sold and taken to Birtwick Park. I was put in a clean, airy stable with a friendly little gray pony and a tall chestnut mare with a long, handsome neck. The groom, John Manly, seemed very proud of me and called me Black Beauty. He would talk to me a great deal. Of course, I did not understand all he said, but I began to learn what he meant and what he wanted me to do. James Howard, the stable boy, was just as gentle and pleasant, so I thought myself well off.

A few days after my arrival, I had to go out with the chestnut mare, Ginger, in the carriage. Ginger had a habit of biting and snapping, so I wondered how we would get along. But, except for angrily laying her ears back when I was first led up to her, she behaved very well. After we had been out together a few times, she told me her story. It was so different from my own. Ginger had been taken from her mother as soon as she was weaned. She was then broken in by force, with no kind words from her master, and sold to a fashionable gentleman. This man held his horses' heads up with a check rein, a special type of rein that stopped horses from lowering their heads.

"I had to hold my head up for hours at a time, not able to move it at all," explained Ginger, her nostrils flaring at the memory. "My master thought it looked stylish. I was ready and willing to work, but to be tormented for nothing but his fancy angered me. So I began to snap and kick. Of course, it is very different at Birtwick Park, but who knows how long it will last?"

I felt sorry for Ginger, but I knew very little then. As the weeks rolled on, Ginger grew much more gentle and cheerful, and she lost the nervous, angry look that she used to give to strangers.

After I had been living at Birtwick Park for some months, my master and mistress decided to visit some friends who lived a two-day drive away. Ginger and I were harnessed up, and James drove the carriage. We traveled the whole of the first day, and just as the sun was going down, we reached a hotel, and Ginger and I were put in the stables to spend the night.

Later that evening, a young man smoking a pipe came into the stable. He chatted to the groom, then went into the loft to bring down some hay. Then the man and groom left the stable and locked the door for the night.

I cannot say how long I slept, but when I awoke, the air was thick and choking with smoke. Low crackling and snapping sounds made me tremble all over. The other horses in the stalls pulled at their halters and stamped in terror.

At last, a groom rushed in and began to untie us and lead us out. But he seemed in such a hurry and was so frightened himself that he scared us more. None of us wanted to go with him. Then I heard a cry of "Fire!" outside, and James quickly came in. He quietly took off his scarf and tied it lightly over my eyes, so I couldn't see anything that might scare me. Patting and coaxing, James led me out of the stable to safety. Then he went back in to save Ginger. Smoke poured out, and I could see flashes of red light. Then I heard a crash as something fell inside. The next moment, James came through the smoke leading Ginger. She was coughing violently, and James was unable to speak, but luckily, they were all right.

That young man had left his pipe in the hayloft, and it had set the stable on fire. Thanks to James, Ginger and I were saved. But two of the horses inside could not be brought to safety. It was a terrible night.

After three happy years at Birtwick Park, sad changes came over us.

One night, I was fast asleep when the groom, John Manly, ran into the stable and cried, "Wake up, Beauty! Your mistress is near to death, and we must fetch the doctor. There is not a moment to lose."

Away we went, out into the night. "Now, Beauty, do your best," said John, and so I did. I don't believe that my old grandfather, who won the race at Newmarket, could have gone faster!

The church clock struck three as we drew up at Dr. White's door. His own horse was exhausted by a hard day's riding, so even though I was tired myself, there was no option but for me to take the doctor back to Birtwick.

The doctor was a heavier man than John and not such a good rider. However, I did my very best. When we got home, my legs shook under me, and I could only stand and pant. I had not a dry hair on my body! The doctor went into the house, and Joe, a new stable boy, took charge of me. Poor Joe! He was young, and as yet, he knew very little. He didn't put a warm cloth on me when he should have, as he thought I was hot and would not like it. Then he gave me cold water to drink, which tasted good but chilled my stomach. Soon, I began to shake and tremble. By the time John returned, having walked home from the doctor's house, I had turned deadly cold. I was sick for weeks afterward, and John nursed me night and day.

My mistress recovered, but shortly afterward, we heard that she must leave England for a warmer country for the sake of her health. My master had to sell everything, including all his horses.

On our last day together, Ginger and I sadly carried the master and mistress on their final journey to the railroad station, where they said goodbye to us. Then we drove slowly home—but it was not our home now.

Ginger and I were sold to a gentleman who lived in a fine house called Earlshall Park. When John delivered us to our new stables, he told the groom that he had never used a check rein on either of us. "Well," said the groom, "they must wear the check rein here. My lady will have style, and if her carriage horses are not reined up tight, she won't look at them."

I held my face close to John's—that was all I could do to say goodbye—and then he was gone.

The next afternoon we were hitched to the carriage with our heads held up by the check rein. When my lady appeared, she looked at us and did not seem pleased, but she said nothing and got into the carriage. Though it certainly was a nuisance, the rein was bearable for me. I felt anxious about Ginger, but she seemed to be quiet and content.

Over the next few days, however, my lady insisted that our heads were reined higher and higher, and I began to understand what Ginger had told me. I wanted to put my head forward and pull the carriage with a will as we had been used to doing, but I couldn't, and that took all the spirit out of me and put strain on my back and legs. "If they rein me up tight," said Ginger, "why, let 'em look out! I can't bear it, and I won't."

Finally, it became too much for Ginger. When the groom tried to tighten her reins, she reared up so suddenly that he had his nose roughly hit and his hat knocked off. She was never put with the carriage again. As for me, I was simply given a fresh partner. What I suffered with that rein for four months on my lady's carriage is hard to describe. The sharp bit made me froth at the mouth, and there was a pressure on my windpipe, which often made my breathing very uncomfortable. There was no relief.

I must now say a little about Reuben Smith, who was left in charge of the stables when the groom went to London on the master's business. Reuben was gentle in his management of horses, but he had one great fault: a forgetful and careless nature. Reuben had nearly lost his job in the past because of his lazy ways, and he had promised faithfully that he would be more responsible. I was unlucky enough to be in his care when he got careless again.

One spring day, he left me at the hotel stables while he ran errands in town. He told the groom to have me ready for him at four o'clock, but it was nearly nine o'clock when he called for me, having run into friends and lost track of time. A nail in one of my front shoes had started to come loose, and the groom told Reuben that it needed looking at. Reuben was too hurried to care, so we set off into the night without further delay. He urged me into a gallop, and we traveled far and fast. At last, my shoe came off. Reuben did not notice, and my shoeless foot suffered dreadfully. The hoof was split and the inside flesh was cut.

No horse can keep his footing under such circumstances! I stumbled and fell on both my knees, and Reuben was flung off with great force.

After one slight effort to rise, he did not move
again. We were far from any town, and it was nearly
midnight before men from Earlshall came to find out
what had become of us.

Reuben Smith died that night, poor man.
Because of his rough riding, my knees were scarred
and ugly, and I was no longer fit to work in a
gentleman's stables. I was sold and taken from
Earlshall without even having a chance to say
goodbye to Ginger.

I became a job horse, which means that I was hired out to all sorts of people. As I was good-tempered and gentle, I think I was more often let out to ignorant drivers than some of the other horses, because I could be depended upon.

One day, I went out in a carriage with a careless driver who let the reins lie easily on my back, while his own hands rested lazily on his knees. There were loose stones on the road, but he never thought it worthwhile to drive on the smooth parts. The result was that I got a stone in my foot. Any good driver would have seen immediately that something was wrong. But this man was laughing and talking with his passengers, and with every step, the stone became more firmly wedged in my foot. The driver finally noticed I was limping and complained that I was lame.

Just then, a farmer rode up and said, "I beg your pardon, sir, but your horse looks as if he has a stone in his shoe. If you will allow me, I will look at his foot."

Sure enough, the farmer found the offending stone, carefully dislodged it with a stone-pick, and showed it to the driver.

"Well!" said my driver. "I never knew that horses picked up stones before!"

"Didn't you?" said the farmer, rather scornfully. "They do, and if you don't want to lame your horse, you must look sharp and get them out quickly. If I might advise, sir, you had better drive him gently for a while. The foot is a good deal hurt."

Then, mounting his own horse and raising his hat, the farmer trotted off.

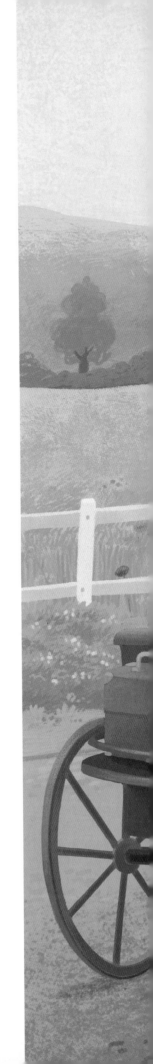

My driver began to flop the reins about as before, so I knew that I was to go on. And, of course, I did, glad at least that the farmer knew about horses and that the stone was gone.

After some months of working in this way, I was put up for sale at a horse fair. No doubt such a place is very amusing to those who have nothing to lose. At any rate, there is plenty to see.

There were long strings of young horses from the country, shaggy little Welsh ponies, hundreds of cart horses of all sorts, with their long tails braided up and tied with scarlet cord, and a good many like myself, handsome and high-bred, but who had suffered an accident or had some blemish. There were some splendid horses in their prime and fit for anything, but in the background, there were a number of poor animals broken down by hard work. These were sad sights for a horse to look upon and wonder if he may come to be in the same state. I was put with some useful-looking horses, and a good many people came to look at us. The gentlemen always turned from me when they saw my scarred knees.

There was one man who seemed interested in me, and I could tell that I would be happy with him. He was not a gentleman. He was rather a small man and quick in all his movements. I knew in a moment, by the way he handled me, that he was used to horses. He spoke gently, and his gray eyes had a kind, cheery look in them.

He offered a small sum of money for me, but that was refused. Then a very hard-looking, loud-voiced man came. I was dreadfully afraid this man would buy me. I could not help reaching out my head toward the gray-eyed man. He stroked my face gently. "Well, old chap," he said, "I think we'll suit each other."

He paid a good amount of money on the spot, and half an hour later, we were on our way to London, through pleasant lanes and country roads, till in the twilight we reached the great city.

My new master was Jeremiah Baker, but since everyone called him Jerry, I will do the same. He was married to Polly, and they had two children: Harry, who was nearly twelve years old, and Dorothy, or Dolly as they called her, who was eight. Jerry had a cab and drove two horses, one in the mornings and one in the afternoons. In this way, each horse got a proper rest. And he never worked on a Sunday. It was his golden rule. Even when his most loyal customers asked him to work then, he would say, "I used to work seven days, but it was too hard for me and too hard for my horses. They need rest, and I need to spend Sunday with my wife and children."

The first week of my life as a cab horse was very trying. I was not used to London, and the noise, the hurry, and the crowds of horses, carts, and carriages made me feel anxious and harassed. But I soon found that I could trust my driver, and then I relaxed and got used to the bustle of the city. In a short time, my master and I understood each other as well as a man and a horse could ever do.

Jerry was a good driver, and even better, he thought as much of his horses as he did of himself. He soon found out that I was willing to work and do my best, and I believe his whip was more frequently at rest by his side than in his hand. In the stable, too, he did all that he could for our comfort. He kept us very clean and gave us as much change of food as he could, and always plenty of it. Not only that, but he always made sure we had enough clean, fresh water for both night and day. But the very best thing of all was our Sundays of rest.

One day, while we were waiting outside one of the parks, a shabby old cab drove up beside ours. The horse was an old worn-out chestnut, with an ill-kept coat and bones that showed plainly through it. The horse's knees knuckled over, and her forelegs were very unsteady. There was a hopeless look in her eyes that I could not help noticing. Then, as I was wondering where I had seen that horse before, she looked straight at me and said, "Black Beauty, is that you?"

It was Ginger, but how she had changed! Her neck was lank, her legs were swollen, her joints were grown out of shape with hard work, and her face, once so full of spirit and life, was now full of suffering. Our drivers were standing together a little way off, so I sidled up to her so that we might have a little quiet talk. It was a sad tale that she had to tell.

Ginger was sold the year after I left Earlshall. For a while, all was well, but then her breathing got bad—no doubt the result of being reined up so tightly in her youth—and she was sold again and again, until she was bought by a man who kept cabs and horses and hired them out.

"You look well off, and I am glad of it," said Ginger, "but I could not tell you what my life has been. They work me hard all the week with not a day's rest."

I was very much troubled, and I put my nose up to hers. But I could say nothing to comfort her. Just then her driver appeared, and with a tug at her mouth, he drove her away.

A short time after this, a cart with a dead horse in it passed our cabstand. It was a chestnut horse with a long, thin neck. I believe it was Ginger. I hope it was, for then her troubles would have been over.

There came a day when Jerry and I did work on a Sunday, and this is how it happened.

One Sunday morning, Jerry was cleaning me in the yard when his wife, Polly, rushed up to him.

"My dear," she said, "my friend Dinah Brown has just had a letter to say that her mother is dangerously ill, and she must go to her immediately. She lives more than ten miles away, out in the country. The train doesn't take Dinah all the way there, so she would have a long walk, with her young baby, too. She asks if you would take her in your cab."

"Well, Polly, you know it goes against my golden rule," said Jerry hesitantly, "but we should do for other people as we would like them to do for us, so you may tell Dinah that I'll be ready for her at ten."

I was chosen for the job, and at ten o'clock on the dot, we started out. It was a fine May day, and the sweet country air was as good in my nostrils as it was in the old days.

When we reached Dinah's family home, which was a small farmhouse close to a meadow, a young man offered to tie me up in the cowshed, apologizing that he had no better stable to offer.

"That's kind," said Jerry, "but there is nothing my horse would like so well as to have an hour or two in your beautiful meadow. It would be a rare treat for him."

The young man happily agreed to this plan. When my harness was taken off, I did not know what I should do first: whether to eat the grass, or roll over on my back, or lie down and rest, or have a gallop across the meadow out of sheer spirits at being free. So I took turns doing everything! Jerry seemed to be quite as happy as I was and took it easy under a shady tree until it was time for us to take Dinah back to London.

The following Christmas and New Year were very merry for some people, but for me and my master, they brought sadness and a parting. Late-night working, with snow, sleet, or heavy rain every day, took its toll on us both. Jerry caught bronchitis and became dangerously ill. When he got better, his doctor said that he must never go back to cab work if he wished to be an old man. So Jerry and the family moved to the country, where he took a job as a coachman. His cab and horses were sold. It was the saddest day of all for me.

At the horse sale, I now found myself in the company of the old, lame, and sick horses. After three years of cab work, I was not the horse that I had been. Many men looked at me and turned away. Then an old gentleman approached with a young boy by his side. I saw his eye rest on me, and I pricked my ears and looked at him.

"There's a horse, Willie, that has known better days," he said to the boy.

"Poor old fellow! Couldn't you buy him and make him young again, as you did with our horse, Ladybird?" asked the boy.

The old gentleman laughed. Then he felt my legs, looked at my mouth, and asked to see me trot around. To my great joy, he bought me.

And that is how I came to my last home. The old gentleman gave me to three ladies in the neighborhood who needed a good, safe horse to pull their carriage. And their groom turned out to be Joe Green, the stable boy at Birtwick Park from all those years ago, now a confident young man.

I have been living in this happy place a whole year. Joe is the best of grooms, clever and with always a kind word. My work is easy, and my strength and spirit are returning. My ladies have promised that I shall never be sold, and so I have nothing to fear. So here my story ends.